Biology CE/KS3
Write Your Own Notes

Name: ____________

Form: ____________

AF172847

Plants & Photosynthesis

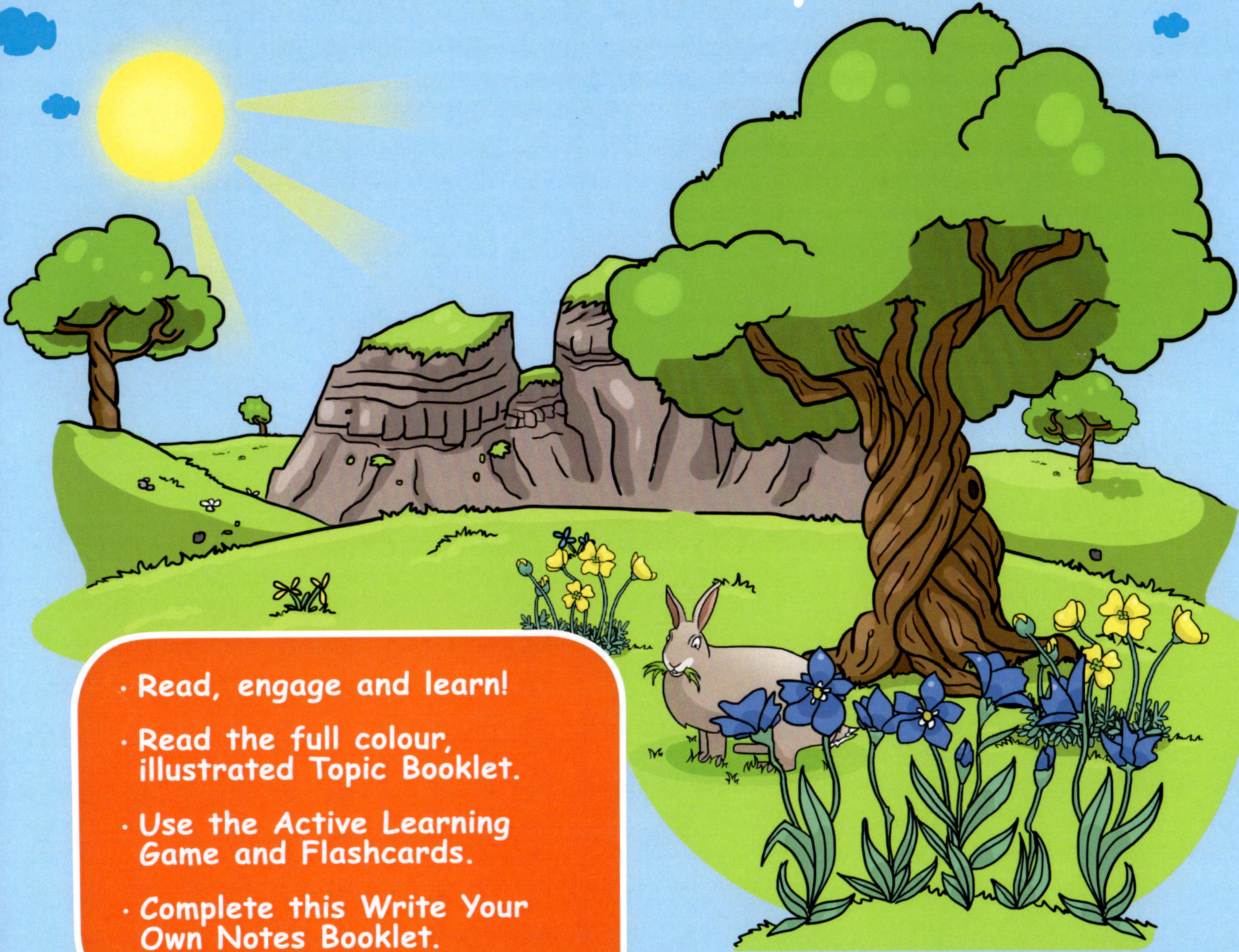

- Read, engage and learn!
- Read the full colour, illustrated Topic Booklet.
- Use the Active Learning Game and Flashcards.
- Complete this Write Your Own Notes Booklet.

This Oaka™ Books Write Your Own Notes Booklet goes hand in hand with the Active Learning Pack on this topic. The pack includes a Topic Booklet, an Active Learning Game and Question & Answer flashcards.

Fresh Focus on Learning

Oaka™ BOOKS

Plants & Photosynthesis Glossary

Biomass: ....
....
....
....

Diffusion: ....
....
....
....

Biofuel: ....
....
....
....

Fertile Soil: ....
....
....
....

Biological Catalysts (enzymes): ....
....
....
....

Fossil Fuels: ....
....
....
....

Carbon Cycle: ....
....
....
....
....

Guard Cells: ....
....
....
....
....

Carbon Dioxide: ....
....
....
....
....

Glucose: ....
....
....
....

Cell Wall: ....
....
....
....

Large Vacuole: ....
....
....

Chlorophyll: ....
....
....
....
....

Magnesium: ....
....
....
....

Chloroplasts: ....
....

Membrane: ....
....
....

Crude Oil: ....
....
....

Minerals: ....
....
....

Plants & Photosynthesis Glossary

Mitochondria: ....
....
....
....
....

MRS GREN: ....
....
....
....
....

Nitrates: ....
....
....
....
....

Nitrogen Cycle: ....
....
....
....
....
....

NPK Fertilisers: ....
....
....
....
....

Nucleus: ....
....
....
....
....

Osmosis: ....
....
....
....
....
....

Palisade Cells: ....
....
....
....
....
....
....

Photosynthesis: ....
....
....
....
....

Respiration: ....
....
....
....

Rock Cycle: ....
....
....
....

Root Hair Cell: ....
....
....
....
....
....

Starch: ....
....
....
....

Stomata: ....
....
....
....

Transpiration: ....
....
....
....
....
....

Wax Cuticle: ....
....
....
....
....
....

1   Animal Cells

- **All** cells have a .... keeping the cell together.

- They have a .... to control what the cell does.

- .... give the cell energy.

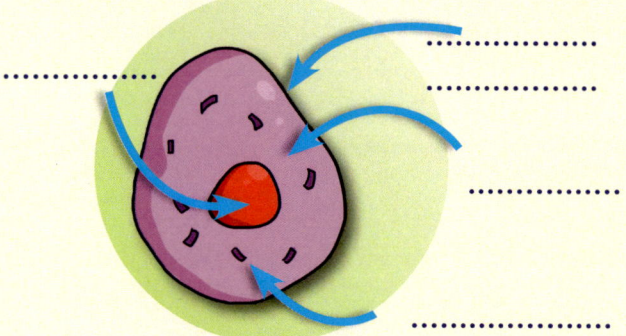

2   Plant Cells Have Extras..

- A .... to help keep its shape.

- .... containing **chlorophyll** for ....

- A .... to help make the cell rigid.

Nucleus

Cytoplasm

Mitochondria

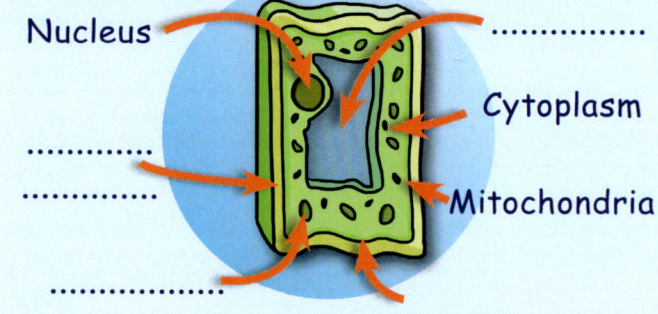

3   Plants Don't Have Bones!

- Animals use bones to keep their shape. Plants use .... and ....

- Water moves into a plant cell by .... This makes the cell swell up.

4   Different Plant Cells

- Plant cells are different shapes and sizes.

- Plants have .... to do special jobs.

- .... have a **large surface area** to .... water and minerals.

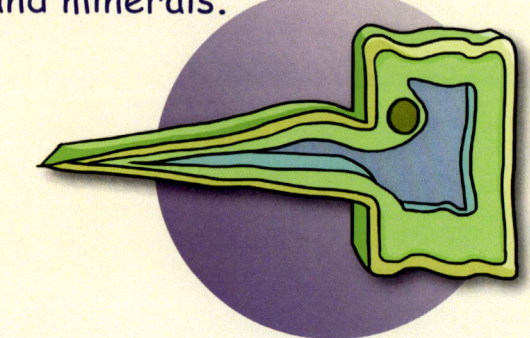

Words to help you...

palisade cells   sunlight   chloroplasts   guard cells   close
stomata   open   diffuses   start   carbon dioxide   food
photosynthesis   water   glucose   chlorophyll   air

5   Palisade Cells

- **Palisade cells** have lots of **chloroplasts** to absorb ....

- There are lots of **palisade cells** in leaves.

- .... look like building blocks.

6   Guard Cells & Stomata

- .... work in **pairs** making little **holes** in leaves called ....

- They let .... in and out.

- When **guard cells** swell up they .... when they **shrink** they ....

Gas .... through the ....

7   Using The Sun's Energy

- Plants use the energy from .... to make their own food.

- This is called ....

- Plants are at the .... of all food chains.

- Plants need .... for photosynthesis.

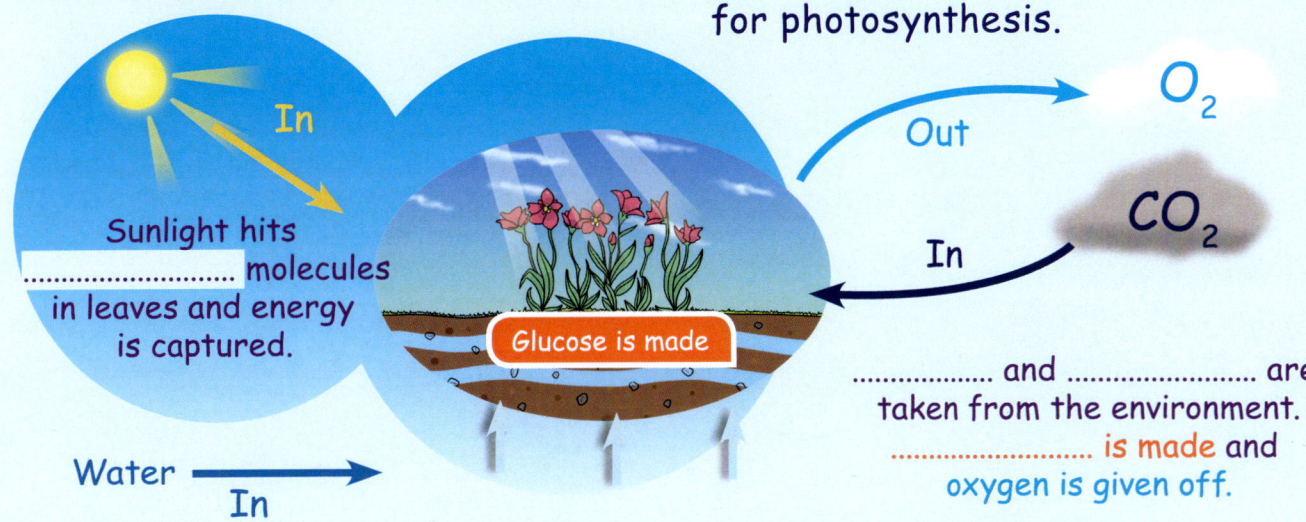

In

Sunlight hits .... molecules in leaves and energy is captured.

Glucose is made

Water   In

Out

O_2

CO_2

In

.... and .... are taken from the environment. .... is made and oxygen is given off.

Words to help you...

xylem   carbon dioxide   food   glucose   chlorophyll
light energy   photosynthesis   water   sun
tubes   leaves   wilts   minerals   phloem   oxygen

8   Putting It All Together

Photosynthesis is important!

- Plants **use** .... from the air.

- Plants **make the** .... we breathe.

- Plants **make the** .... we eat.

- Will talking to plants make them grow quicker?

- Think about **respiration**!

- Complete the equation for photosynthesis below.

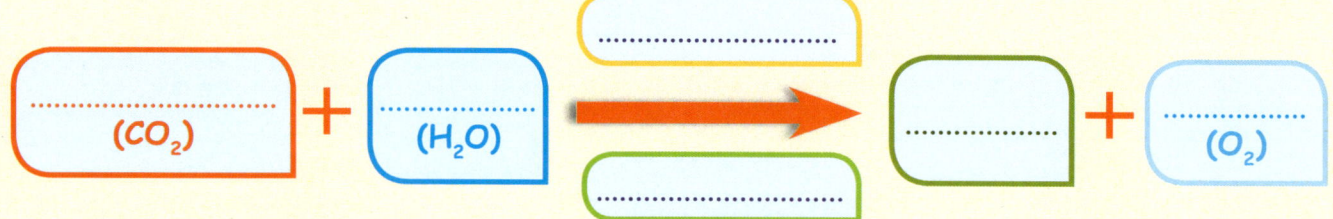

$$\boxed{\text{..............} \atop (CO_2)} + \boxed{\text{..............} \atop (H_2O)} \longrightarrow \boxed{\text{..............}} \quad \boxed{\text{..............}} + \boxed{\text{..............} \atop (O_2)}$$

9   Water

- Plants need .... for **photosynthesis** and to keep their shape.

- If a plant .... it can't point its leaves towards the .... slows or stops!

10   Moving Water Around

- Plants have .... to move food, water and .... around.

- .... tubes carry **food** like .... to growing parts of the plant.

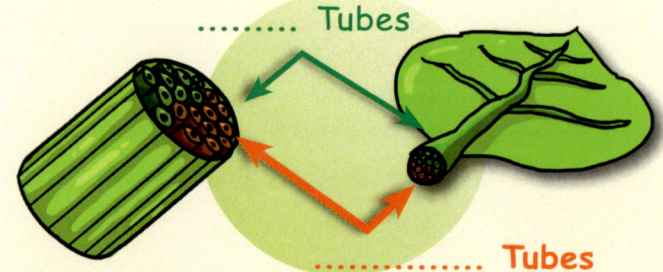

.... Tubes

.... Tubes

- .... tubes carry .... and **minerals** around the plant.

3

Words to help you...

reproduction   stored   carbon dioxide   water   oxygen   glucose
released   sunlight   excretion   energy released   respiration
energy   sensitivity   uses   movement   nutrition   growth

11   Respiration

• **All living things** carry out ....

   (Do you remember **MRS GREN?**
   Life Processes: ...., ...,
   ...., ..., ..., ...).

• **Respiration** uses .... and **oxygen** to release ....

• The energy **released** comes from the .... that plants trap during
   ....

| .... | .... (O_2) | → | .... (CO_2) | + | .... (H_2O) | + | .... |

12   Respiration v. Photosynthesis

• All living things respire.

• **Respiration** ....
   glucose and oxygen.

• **Respiration** releases some of the
   .... trapped during
   photosynthesis.

• Plants ....
   and **respire.**

• **Photosynthesis** makes
   .... and ....

Energy ....
Respiration
Photosynthesis
Energy ....

| .... | + | .... (O_2) | → ← | .... (CO_2) | + | .... (H_2O) |

13   The Good News!

Plants make more .... and .... than they use!

The oxygen that we breathe is all made by ....

O_2

14   Life Depends on Plants!

The food that we eat, or feed to the animals we eat, is made by ....

Life on this planet depends upon ....

15   Minerals

- Plants need .... to make molecules like **chlorophyll.**

- Plants get **minerals** from the ....

- **Minerals** .... in water.

- They are taken up by the plant ....

- .... increase the surface ....

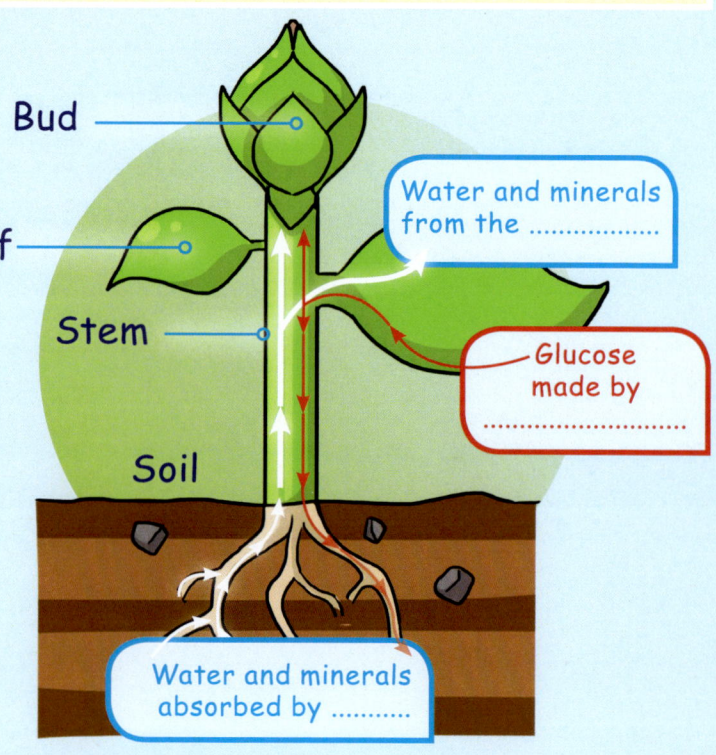

Bud

Leaf

Stem

Soil

Water and minerals from the ....

Glucose made by ....

Water and minerals absorbed by ....

16   Why Do Plants Need Glucose?

- **Respiration** (making energy).

- Making cell ....

- Building molecules & ....

- **Glucose** is stored in ....

- **Glucose** is stored as ....

17   Try This...

- Bread contains ....

- Chew a piece of white bread for a long time.

- It begins to taste ....!

- That's starch turning into ....

18   Plant Biomass

- As plants **photosynthesise** they ....

- Some of the **glucose** they make is used for ....

- The **glucose** left over is ....This is used for ....

- Plant .... is plant matter.

Bigger Plant = More ....

19   Do Plants Sweat?

- Animals .... by losing water.

- Plants lose water too. It is called ....

- Plants lose water through their ....

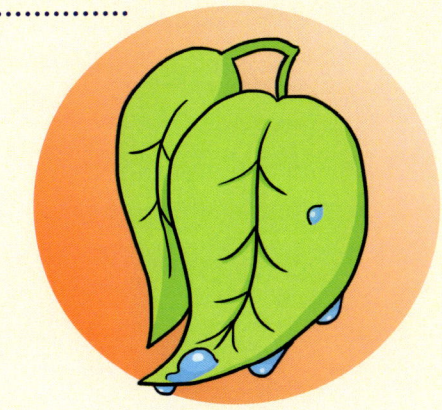

Fill in the blanks using these words to help you...

greenhouses   waxy layer   biological catalysts   water loss
stomata   light   fossil fuels   day   respiration   slows down
plant growth   enzymes   chemical reactions   carbon dioxide

20   Waterproof

- Leaves have a .... (**wax cuticle**) on the top.

- This helps stop ....

- Leaves do not have many .... on the top surface.

21   Night & Day

- **Photosynthesis** needs .... It only happens during the ....

- .... takes place **all the time.**

- On a cloudy day **photosynthesis** ....

- In the winter, when it's dark and cold, ... slows or stops.

22   Greenhouses

Plants grown in .... get lots of light all the time.

- Greenhouses are often heated using .... Which gas is given off when **fossil fuels** burn?

Hint: it's the same gas that's produced during ....

23   Plants Like to be Warm

- All living things use ....

- **Enzymes** are ....

- They speed up ....

Faster!! Faster!!

7

24 Plants Like to be Warm

- Respiration is a .... reaction.

- Chemical reactions happen faster in .... weather.

- Plants grow quicker→ more ....

25 Minerals

- The .... that plants take from the .... may get used up if you grow too many plants in one ....

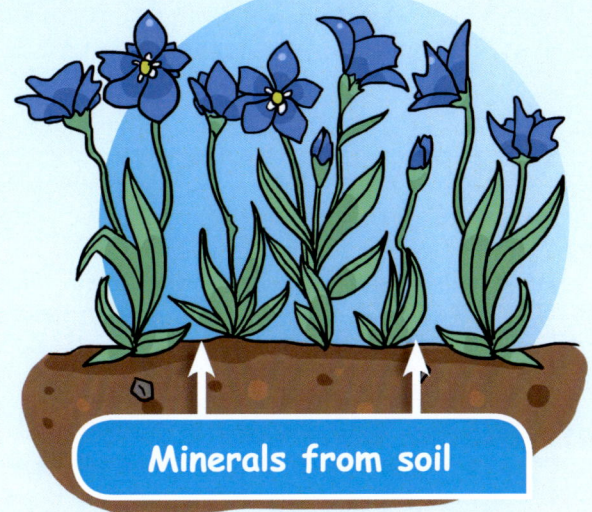

Minerals from soil

26 Fertilisers

- The .... cycle, ... cycle and **carbon cycle** all help to put these **minerals** back.

- But not always fast enough.

Farmers may use ...... **fertilisers** to put minerals back fast.

27 Sick Plants!

- Plants use .... for making plant **protein**.

- Not enough .... = poor growth.

- .... is used for making **chlorophyll**. Too .... and the leaves turn yellow!

28 Healthy Plants' Shopping List...

Healthy plants need...

• .... with lots of **minerals**.

• .... to make cells rigid and stop plants ....

• **Water**, ... and **sunlight** for **photosynthesis**.

• .... to speed growth.

29 Soil

• Plants **do not** use up the ....

• Plants use **minerals** and **water** .... the soil.

Soil with **minerals**   Soil without **minerals**

30 Types of Soil

There are different types of soil.....

• .... (small bits)

• .... (bigger bits)

• .... (mixture of big and small particles).

• .... soil is best for plants.

31 Testing Plant Growth

• Measure .... plants.

• Put one in .... with water and ....

• Put the other in the .... with .... and warmth.

• Measure the ....

32 Loosing Water

- Plants have lots of .... on the bottom of the leaf.

- They let .... in and out.

- They also let water out by ....

Only gas and water past us.

33 Losing water

- Large leaves lose .... of water.

- .... leaves lose only a .... amount of water.

34 Different Leaves

- Cacti have very .... leaves (needles).

- They lose only a .... amount of .... They grow very slowly.

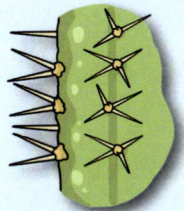

- Water lillies have .... leaves.

- They grow fast, why?

....

35 Finding Water

- Plants take up water through their ....

- Plants living in dry places have .... roots, to find water.

- Plants living in .... places usually have shallow roots.

.... Roots   .... Roots

10

36   Plants for Food

- .... made during **photosynthesis** can be found in fruit like ....

- **Glucose** is stored as .... contain a lot of starch.

37   Energy from Sunlight

- The .... from **sunlight** captured by plants during photosynthesis, is the source of all .... on ....

38   Biofuels

- The **glucose** from plants can be used to make ....

- **Alcohol** can be used as a .... for cars. This is a ....

- Wood burning stoves use ....!

39   The Future

- .... **Oil** is running out.

- .... are already being used to run cars.

40 — Plants and the Air

The air before plants:

- Mostly .... with little or **no** ....

- Formed from the gases given out by volcanoes.

The air with plants...

- A .... **amount** of carbon dioxide (about 0.04%).

- Lots of .... (about 21%).

- Mostly .... (78%).

41 — How Much CO$_2$?

One single big tree uses about 22kg of .... per year during ....!

CO$_2$ 22KG

It takes about 22 trees to make enough .... for you to breathe each year!

O$_2$

The Carbon Cycle

CO_2
Eating grass
Dead animals
....
....
....
....

Words to help you...

respiration combustion photosynthesis decompose

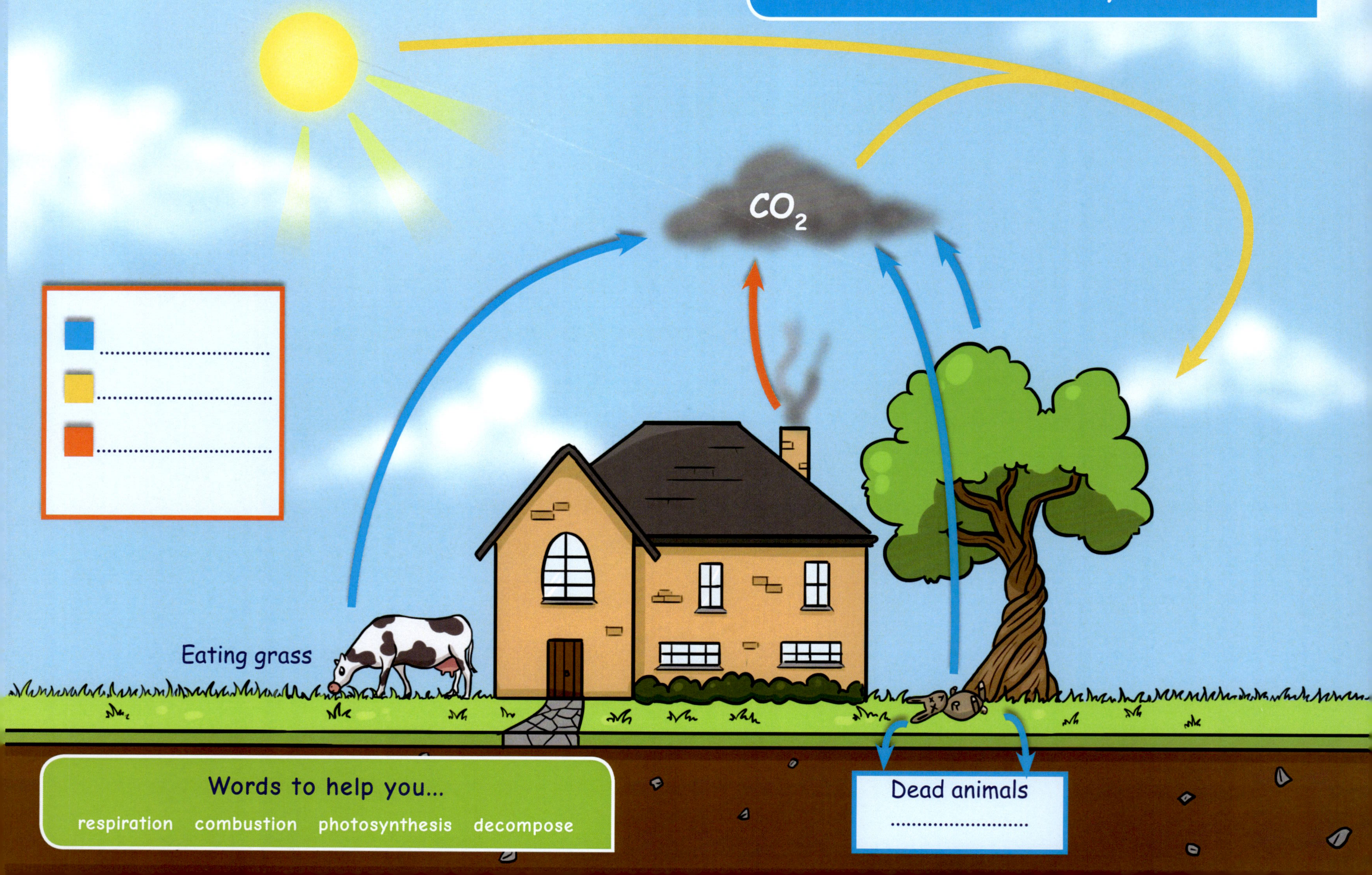

Differences Between Plant & Animal Cells

Animal Cell

Plant Cell

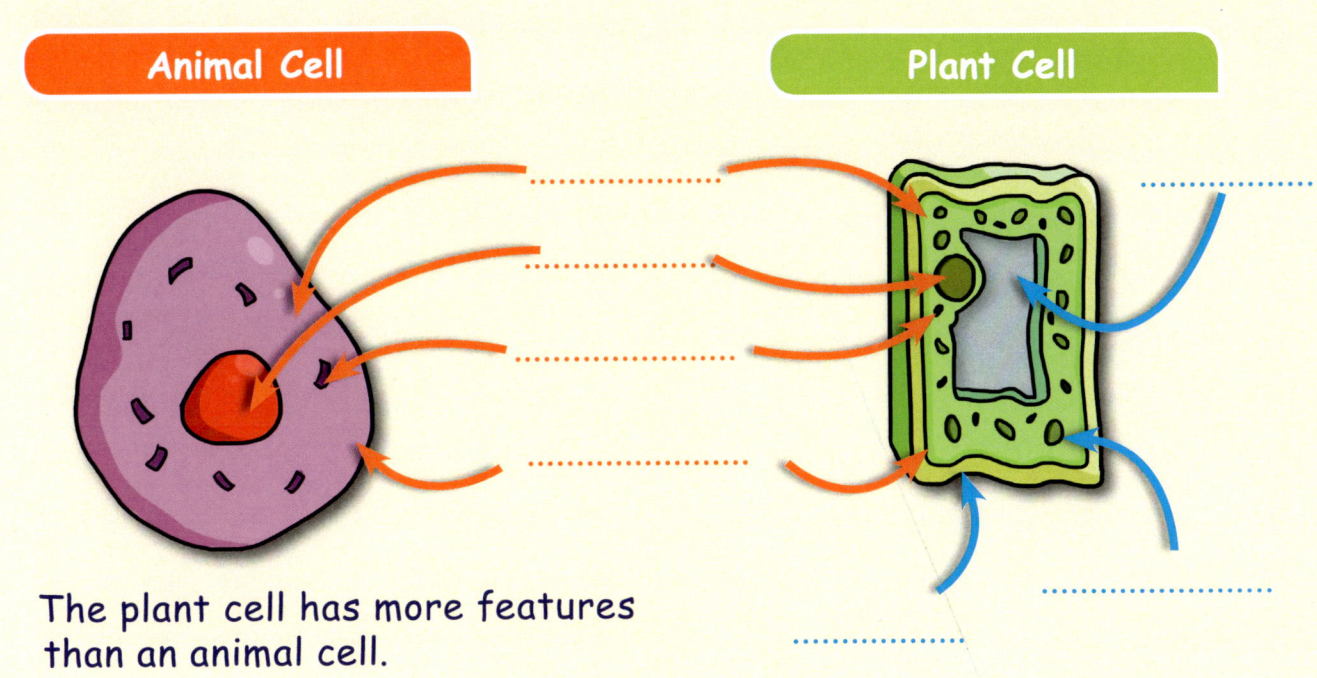

The plant cell has more features than an animal cell.

What is in the Air?

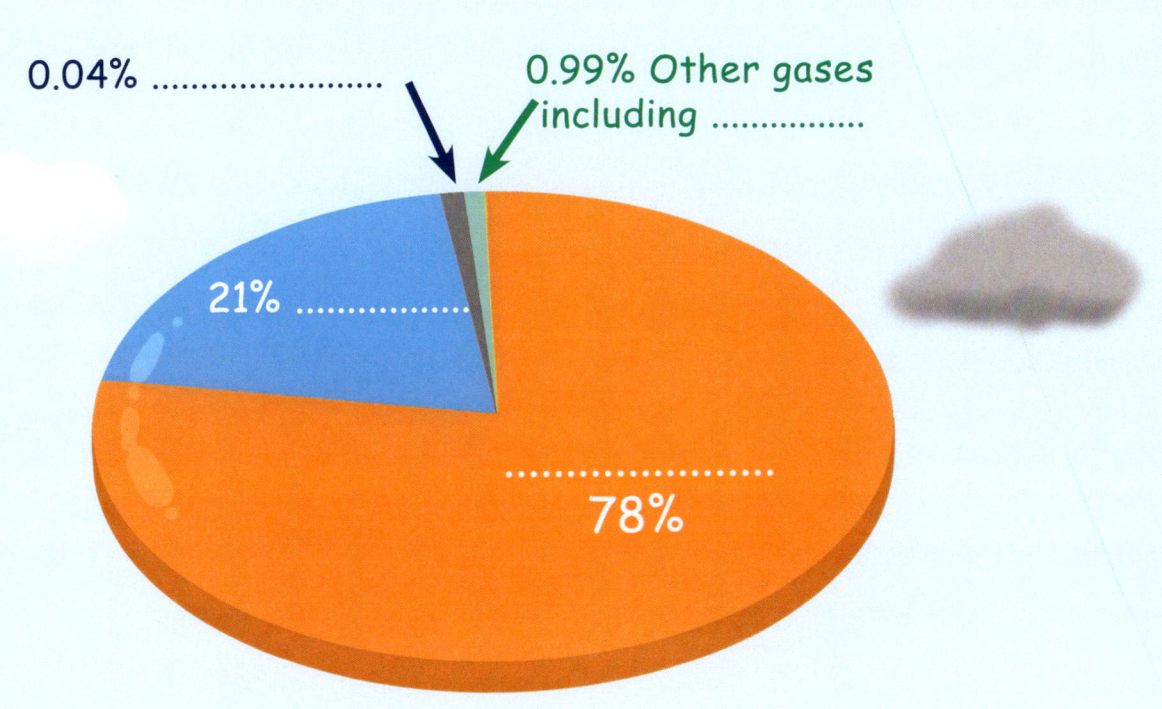

0.04% ....

0.99% Other gases including ....

21% ....

78%

A   Leaf in Boiling Water

- **Put a leaf in** .... **water for about 60 seconds.**
- **Remove it with tongs.**

Be careful! Only carry out this test under the instruction of a teacher.

B   Leaf in Ethanol

- Half fill a boiling .... with ....
- Put the leaf into the ....
- Stand the boiling tube in .... (not boiling) water for 10 minutes.

Ethanol (Put leaf in here)

Stand in hot water

Make sure there are no naked flames as ethanol burns easily!

C   Leaf in Hot Water

- Using ...., put the leaf into the **hot** .... to soak.
- Leave it for .... seconds.

Put leaf in hot water

D   Iodine Solution on Leaf

- Using tongs, lay the .... **flat** on a white ceramic tile.
- Drip .... **solution** all over the leaf.

Drip .... solution on leaf

- The iodine solution will turn .... if there is starch present.

Leaf Cross Section

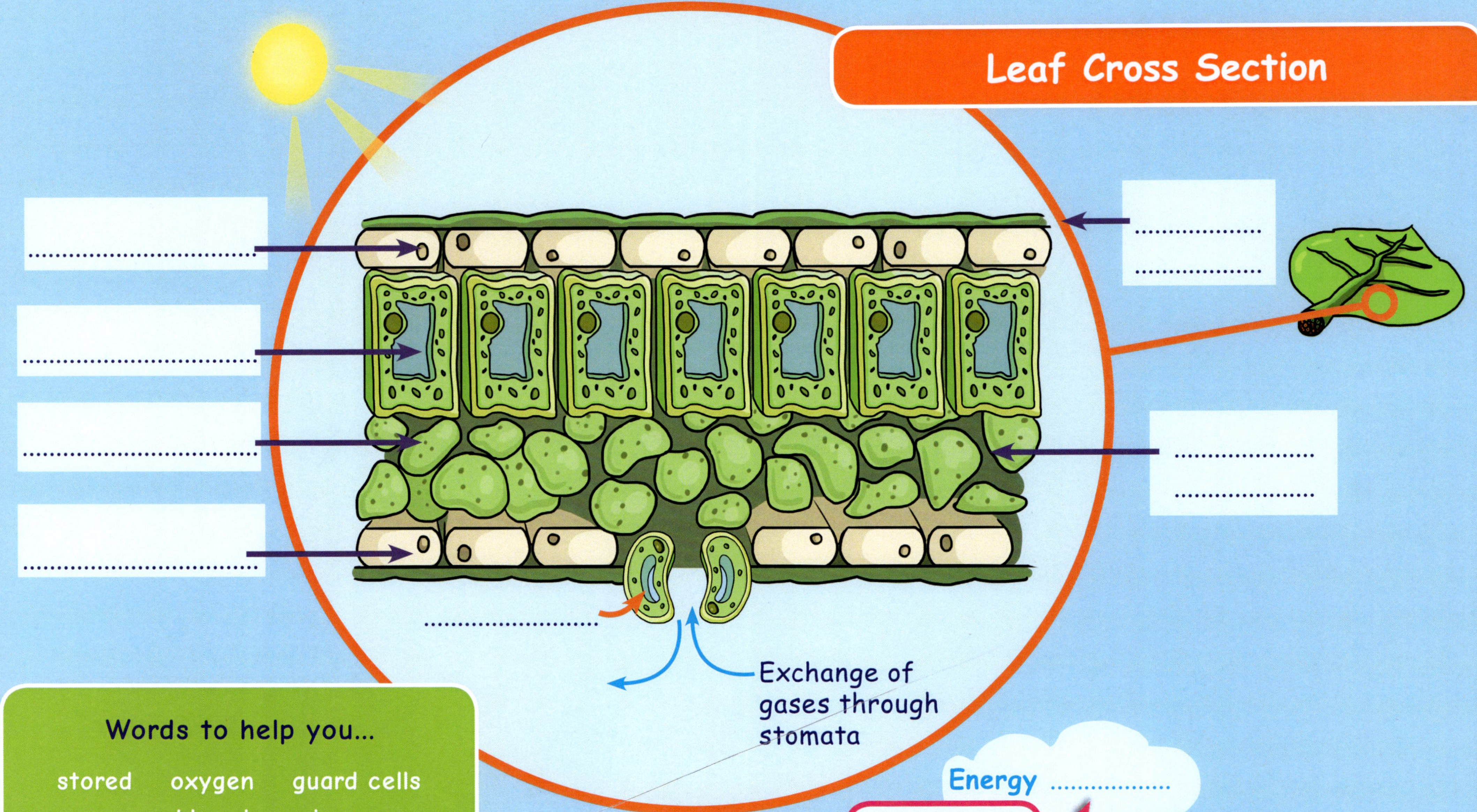

Exchange of
gases through
stomata

(H_2O)

(CO_2)

(O_2)

+

+

Energy

Respiration

Photosynthesis

Energy stored

Words to help you...

stored   oxygen   guard cells
upper epidermis   air space   water
palisade mesophyll
wax cuticle   released
lower epidermis   glucose
spongy mesophyll

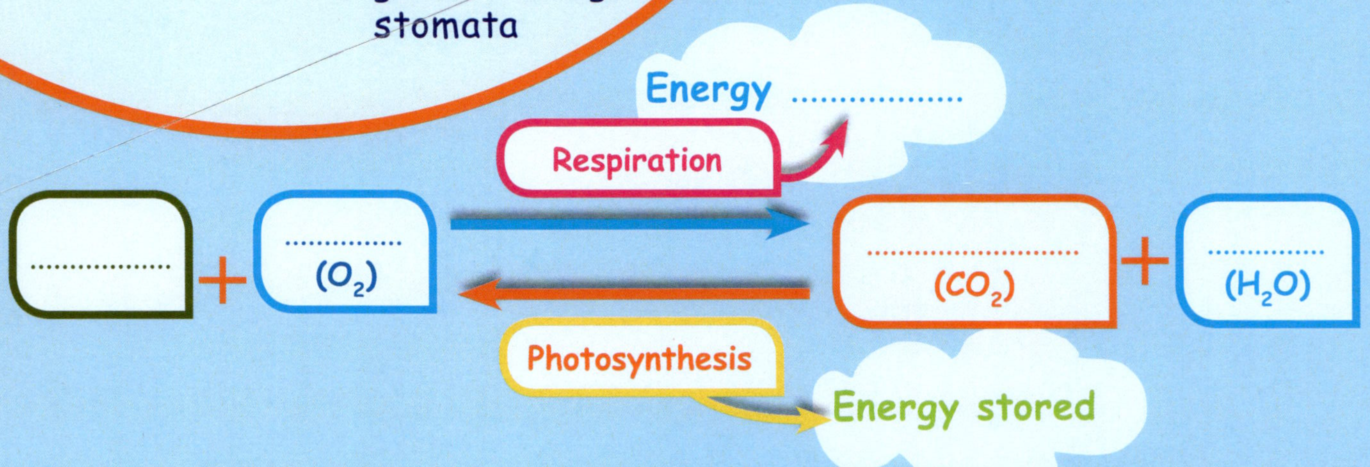

Fresh Focus on Learning

About Oaka Books

Children learn best when they are engaged...

Our aim is to help children enjoy learning by making it fun! That way they will succeed.

Following Common Entrance and National Curriculum guidelines for KS3.

Design and layout of our books follow guidelines from the British Dyslexia Association

Three Easy Steps

Read: the easy to follow bullet point Topic Booklet.

Engage: Play the Active Learning Game.

Learn: When you understand the topic, test yourself using the Write Your Own Notes Book. You can use the Topic Booklet to help if you get stuck.

One (short) Topic at a time:

For some students, a big book is a big turn off. That's why we focus on one topic at a time. Short and to the point.

Reading Age

This booklet is suitable for children with a reading age of 10 ½ years.

Topic Packs for KS1, KS2 & KS3 Include:

History
Geography
Chemistry
Biology
Physics

First paperback edition printed 2015 in the United Kingdom.
A catalogue record for this book is available from the British Library.

ISBN 978-1-909892-55-2
No part of this book shall be reproduced or transmitted in any form or by any means, electronic or mechanical, including photocopying, recording or by any information retrieval system without written permission of the copyright owner or a licence permitting restricted copying issued by the Copyright Licensing Agency Ltd, Saffron House, 6-10 Kirby Street, London EC1N 8TS Tel: 020 7400 3100   Fax: 020 7400 3101   Email: cla@cla.co.uk   Web: www.cla.co.uk

Designed, set and published by Oaka™ Books.

To order other titles from Oaka™ Books, please email info@oakabooks.co.uk or visit www.oakabooks.co.uk, or phone: +44 (0) 2392 388519.

Acknowledgements
Our huge thanks go to the many teachers who have been involved in the development of this series of learning guides. Special thanks to Joy Gardiner, for producing hundreds of illustrations, to Kate Doehren, for her enthusiasm and invaluable assistance to my wonderful daughter Sophie, for being the inspiration for the books and, of course, to Charlie, for believing in them.

ISBN 978-1-911189-54-1

CE/KS3
Plants & Photosyn-
Write Your Own Notes Booklet

ISBN 978-1-909892-56-9

Produced in association with Kate Doehren, MA Ed, B.Ed Hons, RSA Dip, Sp LD/Dyslexia
Head of Learning Support, Hurstpierpoint College
© Copyright Oaka™ Books 2018